When I was a Pup

by Wolf the Dog
illustrated by Polly Powell

Orlando   Boston   Dallas   Chicago   San Diego

Visit *The Learning Site!*

www.harcourtschool.com

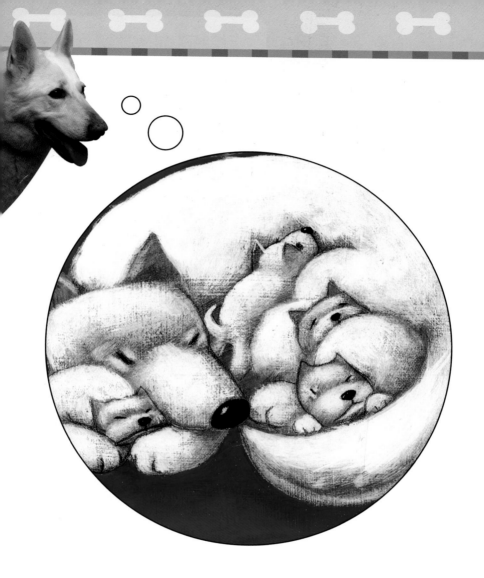

When I was a pup, I liked
to rest with my mom.

When I was a pup, I liked
to go out and play.

When I was a pup, I got a
new home.

When I was a pup, I cried at night. I missed my mom.

When I was a pup, I was
too little to jump for a ball.

When I was a pup, I liked to flip. I liked to jump up.

Now I am a big dog.
I still go out and play.

When I go out, she says,
"Come here, Wolf!" I run
to her.

When I come, she gives me a snack. I could use a drink, too.

When people come to
visit, I make new friends.

When I was a pup, I
wanted to be a big dog.
I like being a big dog.